The tree-house

John and Marilyn Talbot

Illustrated by Bridget Dowty

Nelson

WELLINGTON SQUARE

Contents

Chapter I Nothing to do

Kevin and Rocky were fed up.
They had nothing to do, so they went round to
Tony's house.
Tony had the television on, so they watched
it with him.
There wasn't much on television that they wanted to
see, but they watched it anyway.
'What shall we do?' asked Rocky.
'Tessa and Jamila are going swimming,' said Tony.
'We could go with them.'
But the other boys did not want to go swimming with
Jamila and Tessa.
'We could go down to the canal. We might see a
narrow-boat,' said Rocky.
But the other two boys did not want to watch a
narrow-boat on the canal.
'We could go for a bike ride,' said Kevin.
But the other two boys did not want to go for a
bike ride.

So, they just sat there and watched more television.
Then Tony's Mum came in.
'Why don't you go outside and play football or
something,' she said.
'It's a lovely day.'
'We might as well,' said Rocky.
'We've got nothing better to do,' said Kevin.
'OK, let's go,' said Tony.

The three boys went out into the garden.
They kicked the ball around for a while.
They made a goal between two trees at the far
end of the garden.
Tony was the goalkeeper, and he saved the ball so
often that the other two were soon fed up.
Kevin kicked the ball as hard as he could.
It flew up into the air and went high up into one of
the trees.

There was a loud screech and an angry owl flew out
of the branches and way over the garden.
Down below in the garden Kevin said,
'It was really scared.'
'We frightened it out of its house,' said Tony.

'That gives me an idea,' said Rocky excitedly.
'Why don't we make a tree-house?'
Kevin and Tony thought this was a really brilliant idea.
'But your Mum and Dad won't let us, will they?'
asked Kevin.
'I don't know,' said Tony. 'But let's go in and ask.'
So, they went inside to ask.

Chapter 2 Making plans

The three boys went into the house.
'Mum, can we make a tree-house?' Tony asked.
Mrs Potts was making sausage rolls.
She stopped for a minute to think about it.
'Yes, I don't see why not,' she said.
'Just be careful no-one gets hurt. But you had better
ask your Dad to be sure.'
So, that is what they did.

The three boys went into the living room.
'Dad, can we make a tree-house?' asked Tony.
'Yes, I don't see why not. Just make sure you are
careful,' said Mr Potts.
'Oh, yes!' said all the boys at once.
They were so excited that they were just about to
run outside and start, when Tony's Mum called
them back.

'Do any of you know how to make a tree-house?'
she asked.
The boys looked surprised.
'Everyone knows how to make a tree-house,'
said Tony.
'How?' his Mum asked.
'Well, first you need some wood,' said Tony.

'And some nails,' said Rocky.
'And some tools,' said Kevin.
'Do you have any wood, nails and tools?' said Mr Potts.
The boys looked at each other.
They did not have any wood, nails or tools.
'So, how are you going to make the tree-house?'
asked Tony's Dad.
They did not know. They looked even more fed up.
'Come on, let's go,' said Tony.
The boys started to walk off.

'Just a minute,' said Mrs Potts.
'We might be able to help you. We have some old
wood and some nails in the shed.'
'But do you have any tools?' asked Rocky.
'Yes, we also have some tools,' said Mr Potts.
'Between us we should be able to make a tree-house.'
The boys looked excited again.

'First of all I need to see your plans,' said Mr Potts.
'What plans?' asked Tony.
'Your plans for the tree-house,' said his Dad.
'You need to have plans before you make a
house, even a tree-house.'
Mr Potts gave each boy some paper and
a pen to draw with.
'Off you go!' he said.
The three boys went out into the garden once more.
Each one had to draw what he thought a
tree-house would look like.
Mr and Mrs Potts watched them from the house.
'At last they are excited about something,'
said Mrs Potts.
Mr Potts smiled.

The boys sat around the tree in the garden to
draw their plans.
They all wanted to draw their own plans, but they
talked to each other while they were working.
They each had an idea of what a
tree-house should look like.
'A tree-house should be a place where you can
get away from everyone and be on your own,'
said Rocky.
'Yes,' said Tony. 'It should be a place where even
your Mum and Dad can't come.'
'But a tree-house should be a place where your
friends can come and play,' said Kevin, 'if you want
them to.'
They all thought that these were good ideas.

Mr Potts brought out a cold drink for the
boys because it was a hot day.
Soon they had finished their plans for the tree-house.
They were all pleased with what they had done.
They were ready to go back inside and show the
plans to Tony's Mum and Dad.

Chapter 3 Getting started

'I like your plans,' said Mrs Potts to the boys.
She was looking at the work they had done.
'Yes, I like your plans very much,' she said,
'but no-one has got everything just right. Your roof is
good, Kevin. Rocky, your floor is very good. Tony,
this wall and window are also good.'

The boys listened carefully as Mr and Mrs Potts
talked about their plans.
Mr Potts said, 'If we take the good bit from each of
your plans and put them all together, we will really
have something very good.'
Mr Potts put all their plans together and made
them into one.

This plan had Kevin's roof, Rocky's floor and
Tony's wall and window.
'This is going to be a great tree-house,'
said Tony as he watched his Dad draw.
'It will be brilliant!' said Kevin.
'Yes, brilliant!' said Rocky.
The boys were getting very excited now.
They could not wait to get back outside and start to
make the tree-house.

Mr Potts said he would help the boys get started, but then they were on their own.

'I have to get back to work soon,' he said, 'but I will be watching through the window.'

'Keep looking at the plans,' he said, 'just keep looking at the plans.'

'What do we do first?' asked Tony.

'The floor,' said his Dad.

The floor had to be very safe because they did not want anyone to fall through and get hurt.

'You can use this old door,' said Mr Potts.

The boys cut the door so it would fit well around the branches of the tree, just like it was on the plans.

It took a long time to cut the wood.
'Now what?' asked Rocky.
'I will help you put the floor up in the branches,'
said Mr Potts.
That was hard work too.
They had to climb up the tree and carry the
wood between them.

'Now that the floor is in place, we have to start on
each wall,' said Mr Potts.
As the boys started on the first wall, Mr Potts
left them to go back to work.
'Take care,' he said, 'and remember, don't knock any
nails into the tree, because nails hurt trees.'
The boys were careful not to do this.

Chapter 4. All our own work

'Have fun,' said Mr Potts as he walked back to
the house.
The three boys watched him go.
Mr Potts was going to keep an eye on them from
the window, but now they were on their own.
It was up to them to do all the work.
They looked at the plans as Tony's Dad had
told them to do.
'We need some more wood for a wall,' said Rocky.
There was a lot of old stuff in the shed, and
Mr and Mrs Potts had said the boys could
make use of anything in there.
Tony went in to look.
He soon found something.

'We can use the wood from this old cupboard,'
said Tony.
'Look, it's already got a window in it!' said Kevin.
He pushed his head through a big hole in the
cupboard door.
The other two laughed.
It was hard work making the tree-house, but it was
good fun.

Soon the first wall, with the window in it, was up in the branches of the tree.
Kevin and Rocky held it steady while Tony knocked in the nails.
Then the next wall was lifted into place.
Then the next one.
When the last wall was put up, it was starting to look like a real tree-house.
But the three boys did not stop there.

'Now we need a roof,' said Kevin.
'But we haven't got enough wood to make a roof,'
said Tony.
'Let's just see,' said Rocky.
'There might be a broken bit of wood left in the shed.'
He looked around for a while and came out with a
bit of broken table.
Kevin looked too and found the rest of the table.
After a while, with some clever thinking, they were
able to make a roof for the tree-house.

But the roof was too heavy for them to lift up into the tree.

'I'll have to ask my Dad to help us,' said Tony.

The boys were not happy about this.

They wanted to do everything on their own.

'Let's just have one more go,' said Kevin.

They tried really hard, but it was no good.

They could not lift it on their own.

It was far too heavy.

Tony went back into the house to ask his Dad.

Mr Potts was very surprised when he saw what they
had done.
'This is much better than I thought it would be,'
he said.
Then he set about helping the boys to get the roof on.
Even with help from Mr Potts it was hard work.
But, between them, they did it at last.
Once it was up in the tree they put the nails in
place and made it safe.
'You boys have done a great job,' said Mr Potts.

At last, the tree-house was up.
It looked great.
But there was still a lot of clearing up to do.
Kevin, Rocky and Tony took half an hour putting the tools away in the shed and clearing up all their rubbish.
Soon the garden looked as good as new again.
The three boys could not wait to climb up into their very own tree-house.

Mr Potts went in to call Mrs Potts so she could see the finished job.
She quickly stopped what she was doing and came out into the garden.
'It looks lovely,' she said when she saw the tree-house. 'You have all been working very hard.'

Mr Potts brought out his camera to take a picture of the boys in their tree-house.
'Smile!' said Mr Potts.
They had a lot to smile about!

Chapter 5 'The Owl House'

'Mum, can we have our tea in the tree-house?'
asked Tony.
'I don't see why not,' said his Mum.
Mrs Potts was just going back to the house when
Tessa and Jamila came into the garden.
They had come back from swimming.
They were so surprised when they saw the tree-house.
'It's brilliant,' said Tessa.
'Really brilliant!' said Jamila.

'Can we come up and look inside your tree-house?'
asked Tessa.
The three boys looked at each other.
'Just to look,' said Tony.
The girls climbed up.
'Dad, you did a great job,' said Tessa.
Mr Potts looked surprised.
'The boys did all the work,' he said. 'I just helped a
bit, that's all.'
He held up the plans for Tessa to see.

'Well, it's a great tree-house,' said Jamila,
'but haven't you forgotten something?'
The boys looked at each other.
'What?' said Rocky.
'Where's the ladder?' asked Jamila.
'Jamila's right,' said Tony. 'We only made the
tree-house. We didn't think about a ladder.'
'We could make one quickly before tea,' said Kevin.
'Can we help?' asked the girls.
The boys were a bit tired by now, so they were
pleased to let the girls help.
It didn't take long, and soon they had a really good
ladder to get up to the tree-house.
Mrs Potts brought them all out a cold drink.
Kevin came down the ladder to get the tray.
Mr Potts went into the house and came back with
some food for them all.
They were all very hungry after their hard work.
'This is really great,' said Rocky.
'It's our first food in the tree-house,' said Tony.

'You should give the tree-house a name,' said Tessa.
The boys thought this was a good idea.
'How about, "Mystery Cabin"?' said Kevin.
'Or, "The Look Out Station",' said Rocky.
'I know,' said Tony. 'Let's call it, "The Wild Place".'
They all thought 'The Wild Place' was better than the
other names.
'What we need is a sign,' said Jamila.
'Leave it to me,' said Tessa.
Tessa got some red paint and made a sign for the
tree-house.
It said, 'The Wild Place. DANGER!'

They were all having such fun they did not notice the time.
It was getting late and getting dark.
Mrs Potts came out to tell Kevin, Rocky and Jamila it was time to go home.

As they were leaving Tony asked his Mum,
'Can we sleep in the tree-house?'
'No, Tony,' she said. 'It's too dangerous in the dark. It's time to come in.'

Tony said goodbye to his friends and went inside.
He was not happy.
Later that night he got out of bed.
He could not sleep.
He wanted to look out of his window at the tree-house.
He was still too excited.
The tree-house did not look dangerous to him.

Tony waited until his Mum and Dad were asleep.
He crept downstairs in the dark.
He went out of the back door and into the garden.
He took a torch with him to see in the dark, and started to climb up.

Just as he got to the top of the ladder, a big
owl let out a loud screech.
It flew at him!
Tony was surprised.
He fell back down to the ground and landed with a
crash at the foot of the tree.

Mr and Mrs Potts woke up when they heard the noise.
They looked out of their window and saw Tony on
the ground, calling for help.
They rushed downstairs as fast as they could.
'What happened?' said his Dad.

'A big owl scared me out of my tree-house,' said Tony.
'Are you all right?' asked his Mum.
'Yes,' said Tony, but he felt very silly.
Mr and Mrs Potts took Tony back inside.
His Dad made them all a hot drink.

'That owl had his house in the tree long
before you did,' said his Dad.
'Yes,' said Mrs Potts. 'Like we said, the tree-house is
for you and your friends in the day time, but at night
it belongs to the owl!'
'We should have called it, "The Owl House",' said Tony.
They all laughed.
'Come on, let's go back to bed,' said Mrs Potts.
'It's your turn for the tree-house tomorrow!'